PUFFIN BOOKS

UK | USA | Canada | Ireland | Australia
India | New Zealand | South Africa

Puffin Books is part of the Penguin Random House group of companies
whose addresses can be found at global.penguinrandomhouse.com.

www.penguin.co.uk   www.puffin.co.uk   www.ladybird.co.uk

First published 2014
023

Printed in China

The authorized representative in the EEA is Penguin Random House Ireland,
Morrison Chambers, 32 Nassau Street, Dublin D02 YH68

A CIP catalogue record for this book is available from the British Library

ISBN: 978-0-723-28628-8

All correspondence to:
Puffin Books
Penguin Random House Children's
One Embassy Gardens, 8 Viaduct Gardens, London SW11 7BW

THE WORLD OF
PETER RABBIT™

BABY
RECORD BOOK

Place photo here

Celebrating the birth of

- -

Waiting for you

We first knew you were coming on

We first heard your heartbeat on

The first time we felt you move was

Our thoughts about you and hopes for the future

Finding out more about you

Antenatal appointments

Date --

Date --

Date --

Date --

Names of the midwives and doctors who looked after us

Date you were due

All about our scans

Place photo here

Getting ready for you

Our thoughts about names for you

Boy   Girl

------------------------------   ------------------------------

------------------------------   ------------------------------

------------------------------   ------------------------------

------------------------------   ------------------------------

Some of the new things we bought for you

A picture of your nursery

Place photo here

Your family

Mummy's name

- -

Daddy's name

How Mummy and Daddy met

- -

- -

- -

A photo of Mummy and Daddy

Place photo here

Other special people in your life

A photo of your family

Place photo here

Your family tree

Great
Grandparents

Great
Grandparents

- -

- -

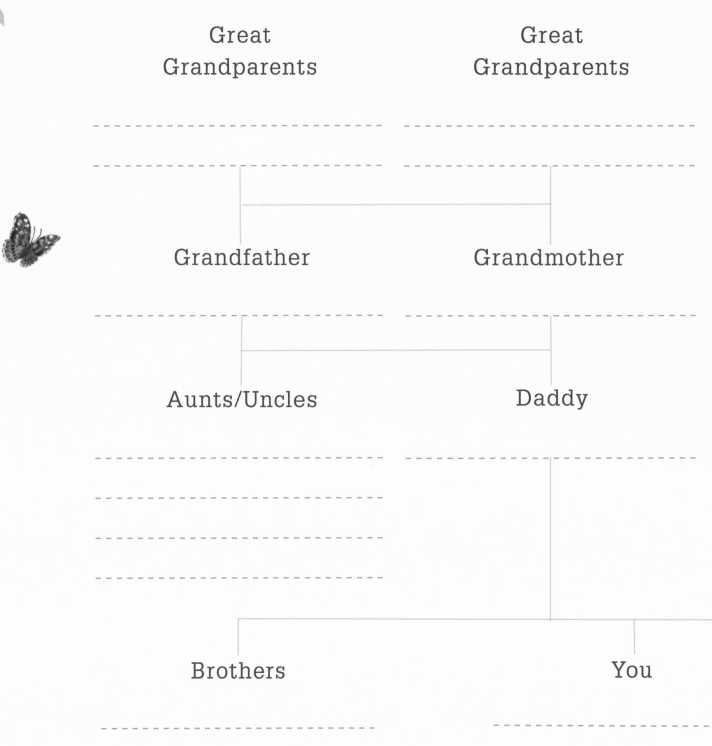

Grandfather

Grandmother

- -

Aunts/Uncles

Daddy

- -

- -

- -

Brothers

You

- -

- -

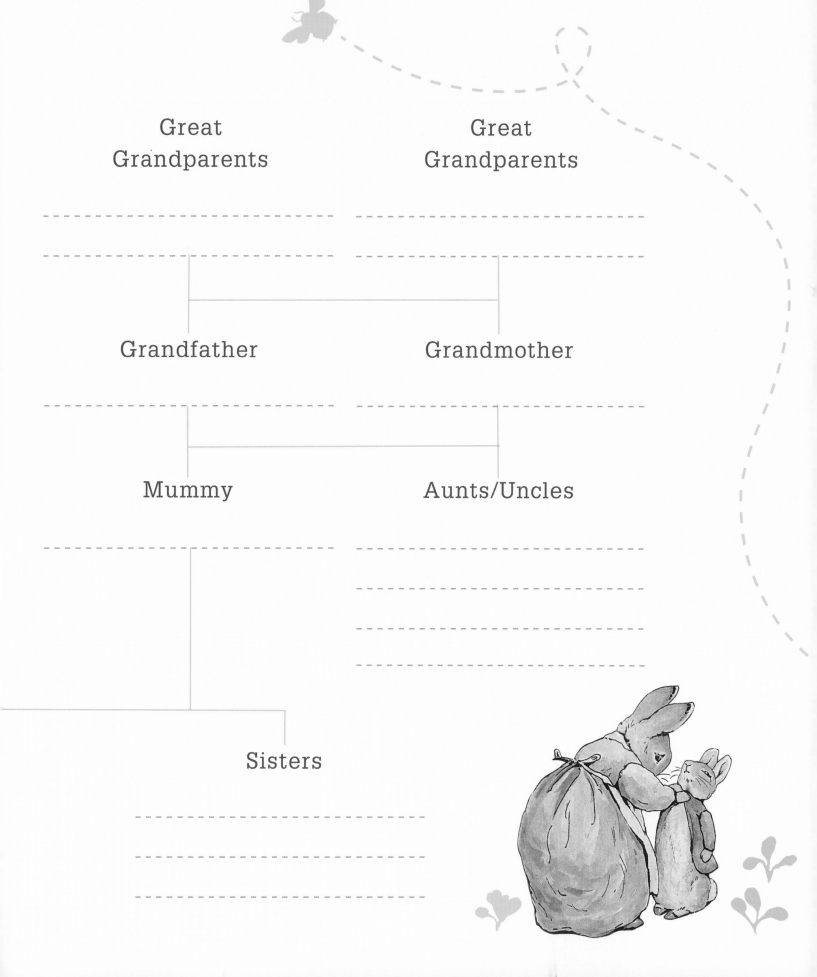

Great
Grandparents

Great
Grandparents

- -

- -

Grandfather

Grandmother

- -

Mummy

Aunts/Uncles

- -

- -

- -

- -

Sisters

- -

- -

- -

Your birth day

Date you were born

- -

Day you were born

- -

Time you were born

- -

What you weighed

- -

Where you were born

Names of the midwives and doctors who helped us

Memories of your birth day

On the day you were born the weather was

The Prime Minister was

The main news stories were

A first photo of you

Place photo here

Our hopes and dreams for you on this special day

Your first day and night

About feeding you

How you slept

People who came to visit us

Other special memories of your first day and night

Taking you home

You came home on

You live at

Our first photo of you at home

Place photo here

Who sent cards, gifts or flowers

Our beautiful baby

Your first handprint

Place handprint here

Your first footprint

Place footprint here

What we noticed about you

Our feelings about our beautiful new baby

# A day in your life

6 am

----

8 am

----

10 am

----

12 pm

----

2 pm

----

4 pm

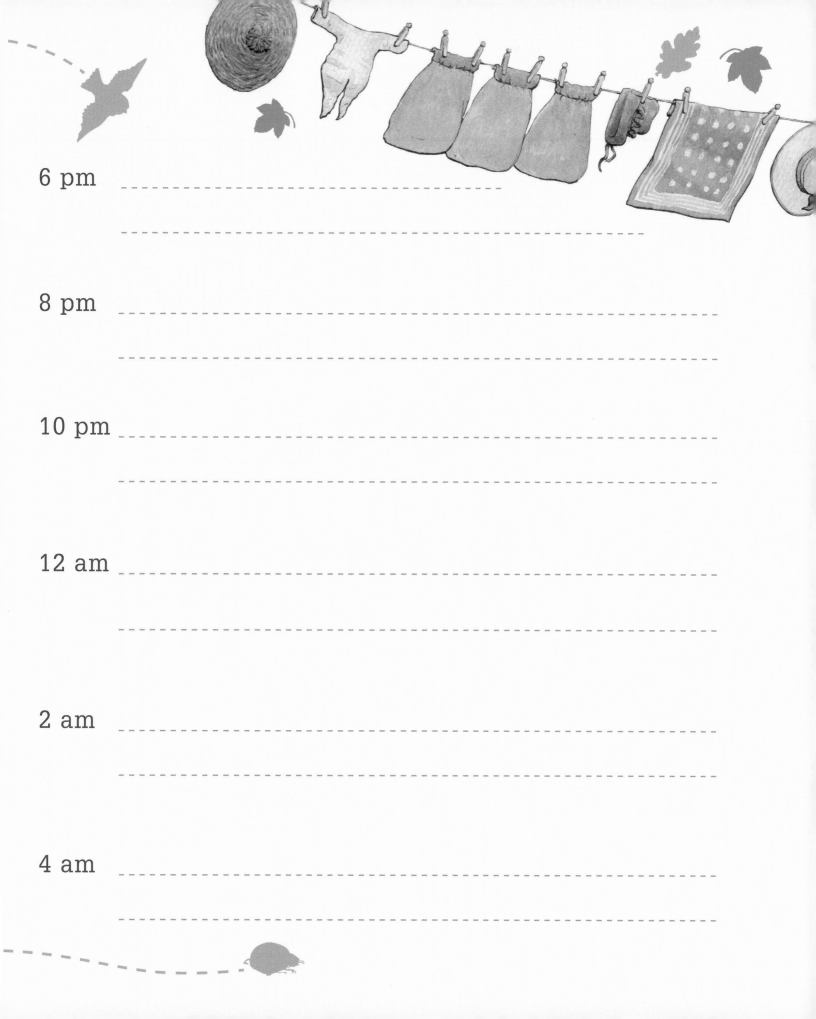

6 pm

8 pm

10 pm

12 am

2 am

4 am

First events and exciting experiences

	Date	Age
Your first bath		
Your first trip out		
The first time we stayed away overnight		

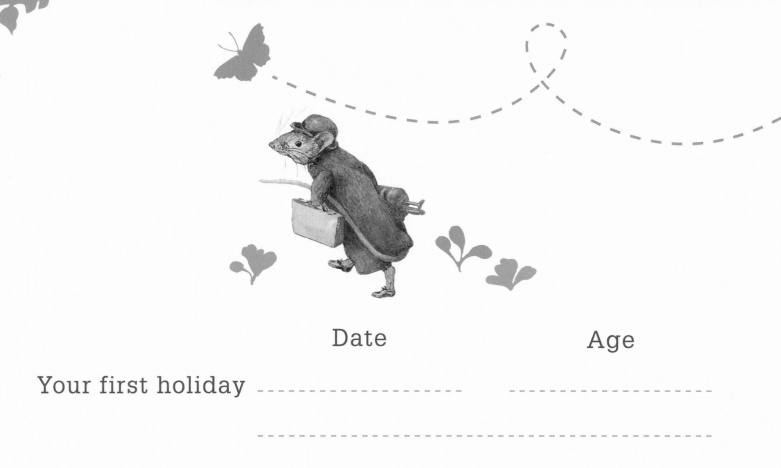

Date   Age

Your first holiday ------------------------------   ------------------------------

----

A photo from your first holiday

Place photo here

Your first friends

Names of your friends

Your friends' birthdays

Things you and your friends enjoy doing together

Photos of you and your friends

Place photo here

Place photo here

First milestones

	Date	Age
The first time you smiled		
The first time you rolled over		
Your first laugh and what it was that made you giggle		
Your first tooth		

	Date	Age
When you first sat up		
When you first crawled		
When you first slept through the night		

Things you love

Favourite toys

Favourite songs

Stories you love

Games you like the best

- -

Food you enjoy

- -

- -

- -

- -

Favourite activities

- -

- -

You are growing up

Date	Age	Weight	Height
-------	-------	-------	-------
-------	-------	-------	-------
-------	-------	-------	-------
-------	-------	-------	-------
-------	-------	-------	-------
-------	-------	-------	-------
-------	-------	-------	-------
-------	-------	-------	-------

Immunisation   Date

----------------------------------   ----------------------------------

----------------------------------   ----------------------------------

----------------------------------   ----------------------------------

----------------------------------   ----------------------------------

----------------------------------   ----------------------------------

----------------------------------   ----------------------------------

----------------------------------   ----------------------------------

Memories from your first year

Your first month

- -

- -

- -

- -

Your second month

- -

- -

- -

Your third month

- -

- -

- -

Your fourth month

Your fifth month

Your sixth month

Memories from your first year

Your seventh month

Your eighth month

Your ninth month

Your tenth month

- -

- -

- -

- -

Your eleventh month

- -

- -

- -

Your twelfth month

- -

- -

- -

- -

Lots of new skills

The first words you understood

The first words you said clearly

The first time you stood up by yourself

Where and when you took your first steps

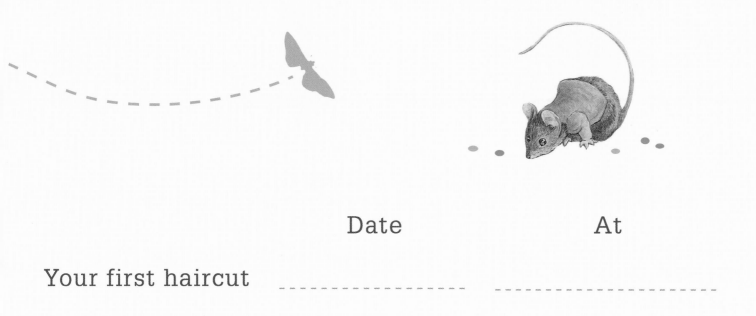

Date   At

Your first haircut   ----------------------   ----------------------

A photo of you after your first haircut

Place photo here

You are one!

Where we were on your birthday

What we did

Who was with us

Your favourite presents

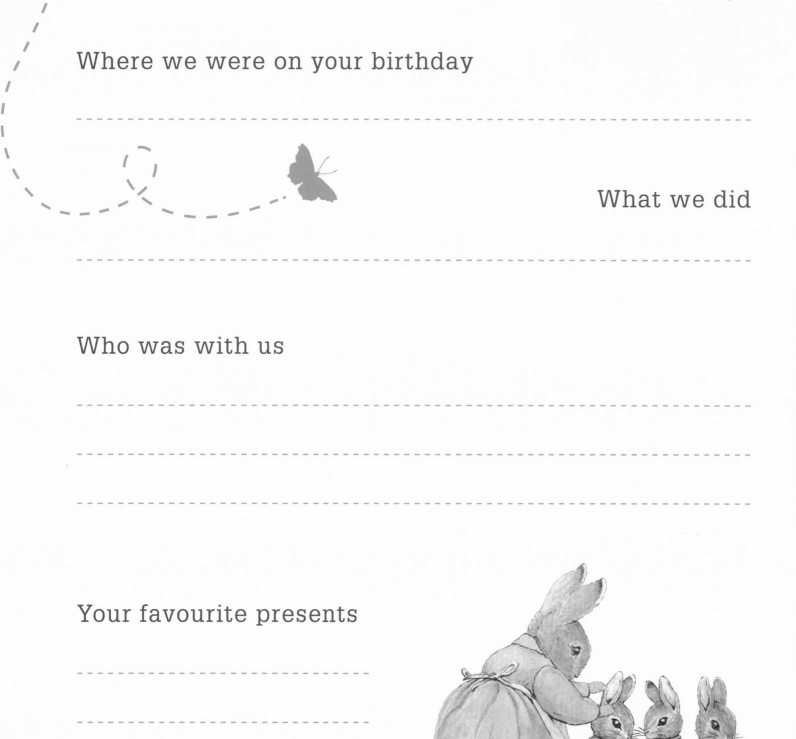

Happy birthday, Baby!

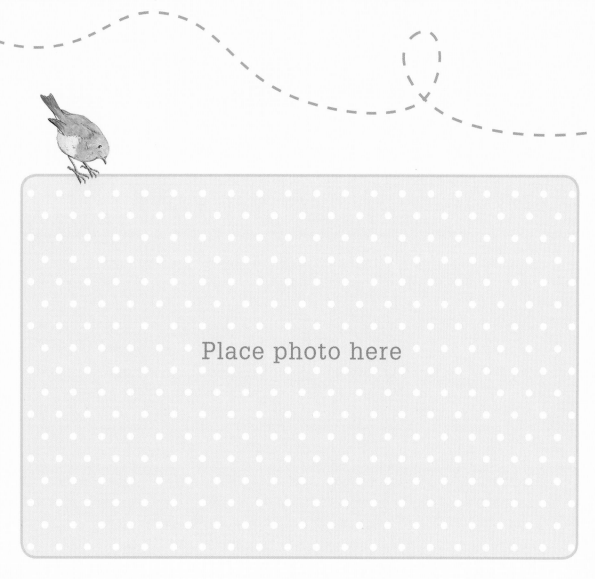

Place photo here